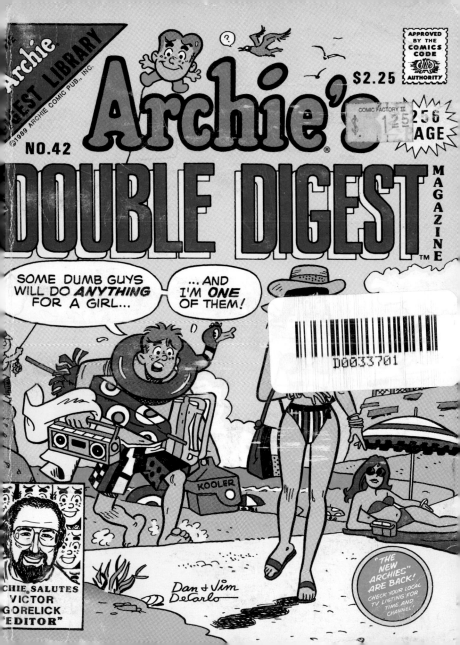

Archie in "MOOD FOOD"

GOOD MORNING, MR. LODGE!

GOOD MORNING, ARCHIE! NICE TO SEE YOU AGAIN!

"NICE TO SEE YOU"? BOY, IS YOUR FATHER IN A GOOD MOOD!

HE SURE IS!

DADDY ALWAYS FEELS GOOD WHEN HE'S WORKING IN HIS HOT HOUSE!

SCRIPT: JIM RUTH

PENCILLING: SAL AMENDOLA

INKING: JON D'AGOSTINO

LETTERING: BILL YOSHIDA

COLORING/PRODUCTION: BARRY GROSSMAN ALISON FLOOD

EDITOR: VICTOR GORELICK

EDITOR-IN-CHIEF: RICHARD GOLDWATER

ARCHIE'S DOUBLE DIGEST MAGAZINE (ISSN-87500671) No. 42, Sept., 1989. Published 6 times a year in Jan., Mar., May, July, Sept. and Nov., by Archie Comic Publications, Inc., 325 Fayette Avenue, Mamaroneck, New York 10543. Richard H. Goldwater, President and Co-Publisher, Michael I. Silberkleit, Chairman and Co-Publisher. ARCHIE characters created by John L. Goldwater. Single copies $2.25 in the U.S., $2.25 in Canada. Subscription rate: U.S., $13.50 for 6 issues; Canada, $13.50. All Canadian Postal Money Orders must be payable in U.S. currency, or by International Money Order. All subscriptions include postage, handling and delivery right to your door. "Archie's Double Digest" and the individual characters names and likenesses are the exclusive trademarks of Archie Comic Publications, Inc. Copyright © 1989, Archie Comic Publications, Inc. All rights reserved. Nothing may be reprinted in whole or part without written permission from Archie Comic Publications, Inc. This periodical may not be sold except by authorized dealers and is sold subject to the conditions that it shall not be sold or distributed with any part of its cover or markings removed, nor in a mutilated condition, nor affixed to or as part of any advertising, literary or pictorial matter whatsoever. No actual person is named or delineated in this fiction magazine and any similarities to real people and places in this fiction is purely coincidental. Second class postage rates paid at the post office at Mamaroneck, New York and at additional mailing offices. Title registered in U.S. Patent Office. POSTMASTER, send address changes to ARCHIE'S DOUBLE DIGEST c/o Archie Comic Publications, Inc., 325 Fayette Avenue, Mamaroneck, NY 10543.

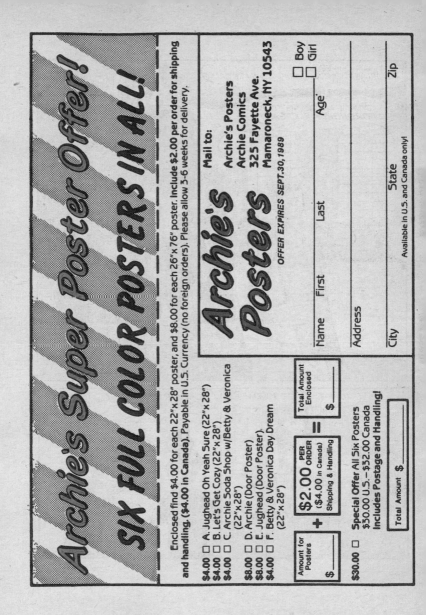

10

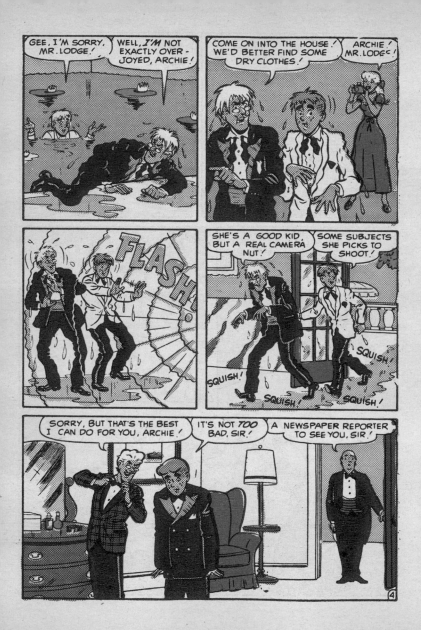

WELL, I DON'T TRUST YOU! FROM NOW ON I'M GOING TO KEEP AN EYE ON YOU!

ARCH, THAT'S A HELK OF A WAY TO TREAT BUDDY!

AHA! WHAT'RE YOU EATING NOW?

A PIECE OF GUM!

I DON'T BELIEVE IT! I DON'T KNOW HOW YOU DID IT, BUT YOU MUST HAVE SWIPED SOME CANDY AGAIN!

I DID NOT!

COME ON! OUT WITH IT! CONFESS! LET'S SEE IT!

CUT IT OUT, YOU NUT, YOU JUST MADE ME SWALLOW IT!

4

7

Betty in "PERFECT SPOT"

ARCHIE, ROW OVER TO THAT CUTE LITTLE ISLAND OVER THERE!

OKAY!

YOU'D BETTER TIE THE BOAT UP TO ONE OF THESE BUSHES!

OTHERWISE, YOU AND I MIGHT BE STRANDED OUT HERE ALL ALONE!

WHAM

DID YOU TAKE CARE OF THE BOAT, BETTY?

I SURE DID!

THE END

Veronica's GAG BAG

Editor's NOTEBOOK

Dear Archie Readers,

Is it next month already? Chee—time sure flies when you're having fun. And having fun is what I've been doing. I hope you think so too when you see some of the great issues we have coming out this summer. There's VERONICA IN JAPAN, BETTY & VERONICA SUMMER FUN, and a special edition of PEP featuring the San Diego Comic Convention. Plus, new for '80, JUGHEAD'S DOUBLE DIGEST and HOT DOG as you've never seen him before... and a lot more.

Now, for your next lesson in producing an Archie Comic. Last month I explained how pencilling is done. This month, we'll talk about LETTERING.

The letterer's job is to letter all the words, captions, story titles and sound effects using different size pens and brushes. He or she also has to ink in the panel lines (borders) and the balloons that hold in the words.

To begin lettering a page, the letterer has to put in guide lines. That's done with a pencil, a T-Square and a lettering guide. By creating these guidelines very lightly in pencil, you can insure having all the letters the same height and the same space be-

tween each line. After all the words are lettered on the page, they are enclosed in balloons with the tails going to the characters that are:

sound effects. The list is endless. Now that all the lettering is done, the pages are finished by inking in all the panel lines.

It takes great skill and creative ability to be a good letterer (not to mention a good speller). Think about that the next time you read a comic book. Next month we'll learn about INKING.

See ya then!

Write your letters to:
Victor Gorelick, editor
Archie Comic Publications, Inc.
325 Fayette Avenue
Mamaroneck, New York 10543

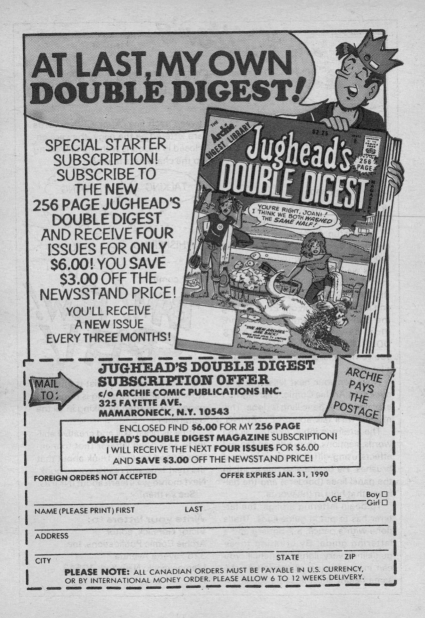